Bud in

Written by Rozanne Lanczak Williams
Created by Sue Lewis
Illustrated by Patty Briles

Creative Teaching Press

Bud in the Mud

Written by Rozanne Lanczak Williams
Illustrated by Patty Briles
Project Manager: Sue Lewis
Project Director: Carolea Williams

Published in the United States of America by:
Creative Teaching Press, Inc.
P.O. Box 2723
Huntington Beach, CA 92647-0723

ISBN: 1-57471-872-X
CTP 3238

Bud gets up.

Run, run, run!

Jump in the mud
with a thud, thud, thud!

Fun in the sun in the mud for Bud.

Oh, no! Up goes Bud
and into the tub.

Bubbles and suds with
a rub-a-dub-dub!

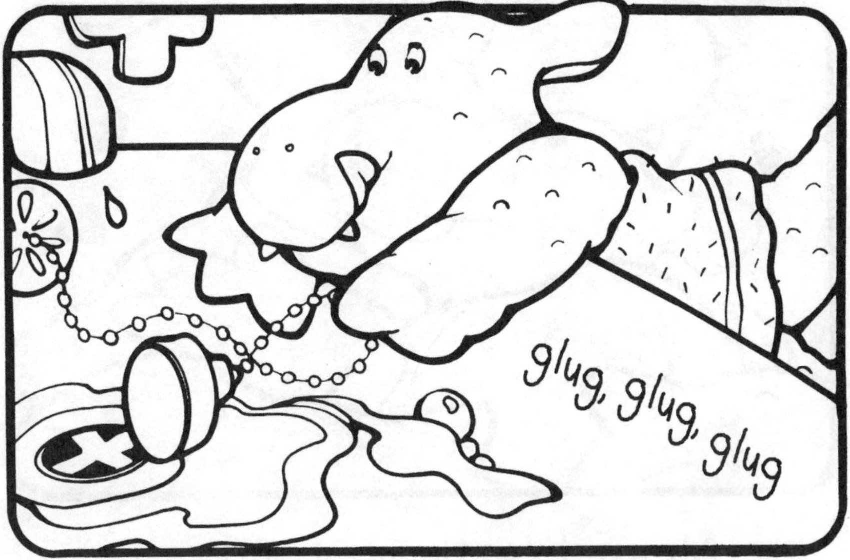
glug, glug, glug, glug

All clean now, pull the plug.

Now it's time for a
hug, hug, hug!

Create your own book!

Use brown tempera mixed with a little liquid starch to finger-paint "mud" pictures. When the painting is dry, add text such as *Christy made a bug in the mud.*

Words in *Bud in the Mud*

Short *u*		**High-Frequency Words**	**Other**
Bud	glug		gets
mud	hug	the	time
up	rub-a-	with	clean
run	dub-dub	for	pull
sun		no	oh
fun		into	goes
jump		all	it's
thud		now	
suds		a	
tub		in	
bubbles		and	
plug			